GW00642641

AFFIRMATIONS & ACTIONS: FOR THOSE WITH
FIBROMYALGIA & OTHER CHRONIC ILLNESSES
Copyright © 2022 by SHANA CRUMBOUGH
PAPERBACK ISBN: 9781735784618

FROM A FELLOW WARRIOR

Affirmations & Actions

FOR THOSE WITH FIBROMYALGIA
& OTHER CHRONIC ILLNESSES

SHANA CRUMBOUGH

I dedicate this book to all of my fellow warriors. May you find relief and happiness in your days to come. Sending you gentle hugs and positive thoughts.

Shana Dawn

Strength

I am strong. It takes an incredible amount of strength to be in this much pain and be able to still function in day-to-day life. I am even strong when I feel weak. That is when I turn into a superhero in order to get things done.

Today I will recognize my strengths and praise myself for what I accomplish.

Pushing Through

It is hard being me. I push through so much that others have no clue about.

Today I will remove or delegate one task from my to do list.

Consistently Inconsistent

Being consistent with an inconsistent body is hard. I am not unreliable and inconsistent, my body is.

Today I will choose one small thing from my task list to practice consistency.

Laugh a Little

Somedays I just want to use words that aren't appropriate in certain crowds. Here are a few substitutes: Shiitake Mushrooms! Fudge Crackers! Banana Peels! Roasted Peanuts!

Today I will find something to laugh about.

Dance It Out

Everything is better when you add music!

Today I will play my favorite song
and let my body move.

Let Go

Living in pain daily causes tension in my body. I am aware that I hold my body as a way to minimize pain.

Today I will take 2 minutes to breathe deeply. I will focus on letting go of every part of my body. I will unclench my teeth, relax my jaw, let my shoulders down, relax my glutes, and stand with my feet shoulder width a part to allow my hips to release my lower back.

Cry Baby, Cry

Crying is not a sign of weakness. It is a release of emotions, disappointments, and pain. I hold back my tears so I don't seem weak.

Today if the tears come up I will let them fall. I know that I am strong, not weak. The illness I have gets weaker by the day and I get stronger. I will defeat this ugly monster that lives inside of me.

Again

Dang it! I woke up today and I still have this stupid illness. I will not always be sick. I will not always feel bad or have low energy.

Today I will look for something that stands out in my day.

_____

_____

_____

_____

_____

_____

Pushing Through

I push through my day at pain levels that would bring the strongest person to their knees. Since pain isn't visible, I have to manage it without causing a scene or appearing too sad.

Today I will not push through. Today I will listen and cater to my body's needs as I do others around me.

Comparison

Comparison is a thief of joy. There may be truth to that. Comparing the person I am in this body to the person I was doesn't make me happy. I miss the things I could do. I miss that body. I miss that person.

Today I will not compare who I am today to who I was in the past. The past is just that, the past. The person I am today is capable of amazing things.

Limits

I am capable of so much more than the limits I have when I am in a flare.

Today I will recognize the limits I have placed on myself and examine why I placed them. Did I place them to avoid pain or did my body place them for me? After I do the work on how to recognize my limits, I will release them. There are no limits!

I Am

My illness doesn't define me. I have a disorder. I am not the illness; I am me.

Today I will remember who I am. List two positive titles that help define you.

I am _____

_____

_____

I am _____

_____

_____

Fluidity

I am fluid. My thoughts are fluid. The human body is made up of at least 60% water. Water is vital for the muscles and joints to function.

Today I will try to drink 64 oz or more of water. I am fluid, I move fluidly, and my thoughts are fluid. Health and wealth flow through me. I move with ease.

Focus

I sometimes have difficulty focusing. It's not because of my brain nor my ability to think or lack of knowledge. The difficulty I have with focusing is based on my illness.

Today I will research and implement a tool I can use to help me focus or to be more confident with remembering things.

_____

_____

_____

_____

Rest

Resting does not mean I am lazy. Resting allows my body to recover from all the mandatory movement, and allows my mind to take a break from mental tasks. I do not need permission or validation from others to rest. Resting is how I survive.

Today I will intentionally create time for me to rest.

Release

I release pain, guilt, worry, stress, tension, bad habits, unproductive busyness, feelings of anxiety, and depressive thoughts.

Today I will release everything that disturbs my peace. I will continue to practice releasing stress as it comes.

Worthy

My worth is not tied to my ability to perform or my illness. I am worthy. I am whole. I am loved. I am healed. I am seen. My illness may be invisible, but I am not.

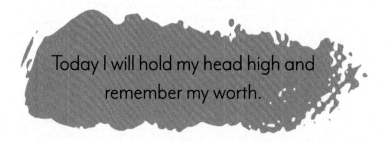

Today I will hold my head high and remember my worth.

Priority

I make everything and everyone a priority; except me.

Today I will make myself a priority and not allow anyone to make me feel guilty for doing so.

Feelings

Recognizing what I feel can be a scary thing.

Today I will allow myself to feel.

Guess What?

My body often feels like I am playing a guessing game, and I am losing! The constant feeling of not knowing what or when something will hurt is exhausting. I am often on edge and anticipating pain. I contribute issues that could be more serious to the larger illness I am already dealing with.

Today I will keep a journal of my ailments so that I am aware of any new symptoms.

_____

_____

_____

_____

Unreliable

I am often forced to miss out on activities because my body is unable to perform or attend. I have the desire, but the energy it will take to pull myself together is just too much. The thought of the pain that may follow a "normal" and "fun" activity does not sound fun at all.

Today I will pre-plan for an upcoming activity. Choose clothes and a hairstyle in advance, shower early in the day, stretch, rest or take a nap several hours before the event, and allow time to move slowly while preparing for the activity or event.

The Person I Was

I miss the person I was. I miss the way I moved and the way I laughed. I felt free. I miss not thinking about or anticipating pain, or thinking about how to avoid it. I feel bad sometimes for not being okay and willingly accepting the new body I'm in.

Today, I will allow myself to remember who I was before this illness came into my life, and find 3 things that are still the same. My old body was not better, it was different; and that is okay.

I Choose

While I am not in control of my body or some of the odd things it does to itself, I am in control of how I feel and view the day.

Today I choose to be happy. I will not let anything get in my way!

Breathe

Inhale..

Exhale.

Okay, do it again....and again!

Today is going to be okay. I am going to be okay!

Enough

I am not inadequate. I am not less than. It may take me longer and look different from what others do, but I will get it done.

Today I will remind myself I am enough. I am capable and I am willing. That is enough!

So Many Feelings

I rotate through a variety of emotions. Some days I am happy and others I can't manage to find anything to smile at. Each feeling is valid.

Today I feel _____ .
It is okay that I feel this way.

Identification

I have an illness.

I am not the illness.

Today I will remember who I am.

Insert two positive titles that describe you:

I am _____.

I am _____.

I love who I am.

_____

_____

_____

_____

_____

_____

_____

_____

_____

_____

Gains

I feel like I've lost some things due to this illness, but I have also gained a lot. I have gained strength. I can deal with almost anything! I have gained the ability to not go crazy at the doctor's office after they keep telling me "your test results are fine," "there's nothing wrong with you," or "there's nothing we can do about that." I have gained the ability to push past things I was sure would take me out! I have gained the ability to self-motivate because sometimes there just isn't anyone else I can talk to.

Today I will take a minute and recognize things I've gained.

Make a list of your gains:

_____

_____

_____

_____

_____

_____

_____

_____

_____

_____

_____

_____

_____

_____

Focus

What I focus on grows. If I focus on the pain and sadness, I will experience it deeper. If I focus on healing and happiness, I will experience it greater.

Today I will focus on healing thoughts and kind words.

List kind words you can say to yourself:

_____

_____

_____

_____

_____

_____

_____

_____

_____

_____

_____

_____

_____

Progress

Any form of progress should be celebrated no matter the size.

Today I will focus on the ways I have made progress. Whether it's my mobility, nutrition, mental health, coping skills, or physical health.

Silver Lining

Every day is not full of happiness and joy, but there's something joyful in every day. I may have to look for the silver lining, but I know it's there somewhere.

Today I will intentionally find joy in something. Write your findings below:

_____

_____

_____

_____

_____

_____

Balance

Some days I am a busy bee and I get so much done. Other days I am slower than a sloth and I don't accomplish anything on my list. On both days, I did the best I could.

Today I will be thankful for the days I am able to be busy and for the days I need to take it slower.

Unwanted Advice

It always amazes me how much advice others who don't have my illness give to me. I know it is sometimes out of the goodness of their hearts, but sometimes I just want them to leave me alone. I never asked for their advice or what their mom's uncle's cousins' son did.

Today I will come up with a nice way to say, "I don't need your advice."

Superhuman

People wonder how I survive in pain every day. Its me! I am people! I seriously don't know how I do this every day!

Scream a Little

Being this sick is hard. It's a battle every day. Some days I throw in the whole towel. Some days I want to just scream. Some days it's just too much!! Adulting, work, taking care of others, wearing all these hats is just TOO MUCH!

Today I will take a minute in the car alone and scream as loud as I can for 30 seconds.

Rain

While the rain makes flowers grow and washes away the pollen, it makes me tighten up like the Tin Man.

Today I will be kind to myself and not push myself past my limits. I will do what I must do only. Everything else can wait.

Inflammation

My body is inflamed. Everything hurts. There are so many theories of things that may help with my inflammation.

Today I will research inflammatory solutions that may help my pain. (i.e: foods or vitamins that fight against inflammation).

Weather

Weather or temperature changes cause my body to flare. I can't control it. I wish I could be proactive, but I can't control the weather. I can put on extra layers or take them off to try and help how I feel.

Today I will not become frustrated with the things I cannot control. I will control the things I can.

Holding

I hold my breath to brace myself for what's to come. I hold my body to protect myself from the pain. Holding my breath stops me from being able to have proper mobility.

Today I will make a conscious effort to let go and inhale fully. Upon exhaling, focus on releasing all tension in your body. Repeat 3x.

Counting on Me

You know who is counting on me to come through for them today? ME!

Today I won't disappoint myself.

Catch Up

When my body is down, I feel like I didn't get everything I needed to get done. So, I catch up on all the tasks and more when I feel better.

Today I will be thankful for feeling pretty good. I will not play catch up because I am having a better day. I will not attempt to catch up on all the things. I will make myself a list of 3 tasks to complete. When I am done with those tasks I will rest.

Focus

Sometimes it's so hard for me to focus. My thoughts are like a shaken puzzle and I can't find all the pieces to put them together. I know what I want to say, but when I open my mouth either nothing comes out or something not smart comes out. Due to this, I don't speak out or take as many chances as I used to. I pretend to be confident sometimes, but I am still very self-conscious.

Today I will speak kindly to myself when I don't feel adequate or smart. I will research vitamins that may help with focus or memory.

Choices

I didn't choose this life. It chose me!

Today I will focus on the good. I will remember the good in me and not allow how I physically feel to effect how I feel mentally.

_____

_____

_____

_____

_____

Mentally Aware

I know mental disorders often are paired with my diagnosis. I am not that. I do not accept or repeat depressive, manic, or panic thoughts or ideas.

Today I will repeat this:
I am calm. I will stay calm. I am strong.
I have coping skills. I use them when I
need them to help me stay strong. I am
okay. I am okay. I am okay.

Protection

My eyes and ears are portals to my subconscious thoughts.

Today I will watch what I spend my time doing and reading. If social media becomes too much or too negative, I will log off. Today I will protect my peace by any means necessary.

Anxious

Anxiety happens when we are trying to control the uncontrollable or from anticipating the unknown.

Today I will do my best to control what I can and release what I can't. I am aware this will take practice.

Calming Box Ideas

- Candle
- Small Pieces of Dark Chocolate
- Notepad and Pencil
- Bottle of Water
- Fidget Spinner
- Squishy or Stress Ball
- Essential Oil
- Book
- Jump Rope
- Nice Note to Yourself
- Notepad and Pencil
- Stickers
- Coloring Book and Colored Pencils or Crayons
- Bubbles
- Teddy Bear
- Ear Plugs
- Audio Book
- Yoga
- Cards
- Activity Book (i.e.: crosswords)
- Playdoh/Silly Putty

Resources:

Exercises: I recently took a series of low impact HIIT type classes. The instructor was Ashley with RA Warrior Fitness. She is a fellow warrior, diagnosed with Rheumatoid Arthritis and Lupus. Being a fellow warrior, she was able to give modifications and motivation during the workouts.

Cardio: I know it is difficult to do any more walking than what you have to, but some form of exercise is necessary to keep your body mobile. Cardio on better days is a great start. Cardio is no longer boring! There are now all types: Dance Fitness, Step Aerobics, Hip Hop Step, and many more you can find on YouTube. You can also walk on a treadmill, ride a stationary bike, or my favorite, use the elliptical. Don't limit yourself!

Pool Therapy and Swim Aerobics: I saw a huge change in how my body relaxed after pool therapy. I highly recommend trying it out. Finding a therapist that had many years of experience working with people with fibromyalgia was very helpful and I learned so much.

Stretching: I was told to stretch every morning. I laughed out loud! However, my pool therapist taught me how to gentle stretch. I was able to do that! Gentle stretching and yoga helped me so much. Below are various types of yoga to research:

- Hatha yoga
- Iyengar yoga
- Hot yoga and Bikram yoga
- Yin yoga
- Vinyasa yoga

The most important thing is to listen to your body, know your limits, and STOP if it hurts.

Consult a medical professional before trying any new exercises.

Grounding Techniques

- Visualize yourself completing the task

- Recite simple addition or multiplication facts

- Take three deep breaths

- Recite or write down your favorite motivational quote

- Look up the 5 Senses Grounding Technique

- Try 3 part breathing

- Recite your favorite mantra or bible verse

Your Notes:

_____

_____

_____

_____

_____

_____

_____

_____

_____

_____

_____

_____

_____

Your Notes:

Your Notes:

_____

_____

_____

_____

_____

_____

_____

_____

_____

_____

_____

_____

_____

_____

Your Notes:

_____

_____

_____

_____

_____

_____

_____

_____

_____

_____

_____

_____

_____

Your Notes:

Your Notes:

_____

_____

_____

_____

_____

_____

_____

_____

_____

_____

_____

_____

_____

Your Notes:

_____

_____

_____

_____

_____

_____

_____

_____

_____

_____

_____

_____

_____

_____

Your Notes:

Your Notes: